THE POCKET # KAMA
SUTRA

EROTIC SECRETS FOR MODERN LOVERS

THE POCKET KAMA SUTRA

EROTIC SECRETS FOR MODERN LOVERS

NICOLE
BAILEY

DUNCAN BAIRD PUBLISHERS
LONDON

THE POCKET KAMA SUTRA

NICOLE BAILEY

First published in the United Kingdom and Ireland in 2006 by
Duncan Baird Publishers, an imprint of Watkins Publishing Limited,
PO Box 883, Oxford, OX1 9PL, UK

A member of Osprey Group
Osprey Publishing, PO Box 3985, New York, NY 10185-3985
Tel: (001) 212 753 4402   Email: info@ospreypublishing.com

Managing Editor: Grace Cheetham
Editor: Zoë Stone
Managing Designer: Manisha Patel
Designer: Sailesh Patel

A CIP record for this book is available from the British Library
ISBN: 978-1-84483-288-0
10 9

Typeset in Monitor
Colour reproduction by Colourscan, Singapore
Printed in Hong Kong

Watkins Publishing is supporting the
Woodland Trust, the UK's leading
woodland conservation charity, by
funding tree-planting initiatives and
woodland maintenance.

www.dbp.co.uk

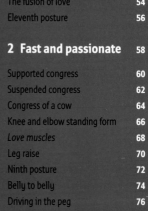

Contents

Introduction

Mention the *Kama Sutra* and many people think of audacious lovemaking positions and exotic sex techniques. There's no doubt that the *Kama Sutra* contains these — but perhaps the most valuable lesson found within its pages is that sex is a special occasion. Rather than relegating sex to the end of the day when you fall exhausted into bed — as many modern lovers do — the *Kama Sutra* treats it as a ritual. You prepare your environment, your body and your mind, and then — most importantly — you take time over sex. The *Kama Sutra* pays attention to the fine details of lovemaking: the way you kiss, the way you nibble or scratch your lover's skin, even the angle and speed at which the penis moves inside the vagina.

WHAT IS THE *KAMA SUTRA*?

Very little is known about the man behind the *Kama Sutra*. His name is Vatsyayana Mallanaga and he is thought to have lived in India between 1 and 4 CE. His collection of *sutras* (a *sutra* is an aphorism) was written in Sanskrit and takes the form of seven books. The word *kama* means pleasure, desire or sex.

Vatsyayana is believed to be the compiler of the *Kama Sutra* rather than its originator. His source was an array of existing Hindu erotic texts. Contrary to popular belief, only one of the seven *Kama Sutra* books is specifically about sex — the other six deal with the mores of erotic relationships, from guidelines about seducing a virgin to how to extract money from a lover.

Although the *Kama Sutra* is extremely ancient, it was unknown in the West until 1883. Sir Richard Burton and Forster Arbuthnot were responsible for first translating it from Sanskrit into English. Publishing erotica was highly controversial in Victorian England, so Burton and Arbuthnot created their own publishing company, the Kama Shastra Society. Readers (mainly scholars and upper-class gentlemen with a taste for erotica) bought the book by private subscription. In the 1960s the sexual revolution combined with the fashion for all things Indian meant that the English version of the *Kama Sutra* not only became acceptable, but was celebrated for its sexual frankness. It was published formally in England and the United States in 1962.

THE *ANANGA RANGA* AND *THE PERFUMED GARDEN*

The Kama Shastra Society went on to publish two more Eastern love texts: the *Ananga Ranga* and *The Perfumed Garden*.

The *Ananga Ranga* was written originally in India in the 15th century by Kalyana Malla. Unlike the *Kama Sutra*, the whole of the *Ananga Ranga* is specifically about sex. Malla includes detailed lists of methods of embracing, kissing, scratching, biting and spanking, as well as positions for making love. Husbands were the intended readership and Malla's aim was to describe all the ways in which men could keep a marriage sexy.

The aim of *The Perfumed Garden* was also to stimulate and maintain passion, but for all men and women — not just those who were married to one another. Written by Sheikh Nefzawi in 16th-century Tunis, the text of *The Perfumed Garden* is considered more poetic, erotic and humorous in style than either the *Kama Sutra* or the *Ananga Ranga*. Its subjects include the characteristics of sexually desirable men and women, the ways in which to arouse a woman before sex, sex positions, and exhaustive lists of the different types of male and female genitals.

THE POCKET KAMA SUTRA

My book combines the wisdom of Vatsyayana, Kalyana Malla and Sheikh Nefzawi with modern insights into human sexuality. The emphasis is on making sex into a whole-body experience in which sensual pleasure ripples through your entire body, not just your genitals.

The book is divided into four chapters: Slow and Soulful, Fast and Passionate, Deep and Erotic, and Adventurous and Thrilling. Each contains a selection of the most exciting sex positions from the *Kama Sutra*, the *Ananga Ranga* and *The Perfumed Garden*, focusing on the practical — techniques that you can try with your lover right now. There are 52 positions, so you and your lover can try one new position a week!

In Chapter 1 I describe how you and your lover can get really up-close-and-personal with affectionate, intimate lovemaking — perfect for when you really want to get inside each other's skin. Chapter 2 has great positions for times when you want immediate, impulsive and spontaneous sex. In Chapter 3 the positions I've chosen are particularly erotic because they offer deep penetration, and Chapter 4 covers some unusual positions — perfect for when you are both feeling very creative.

Slow and soulful

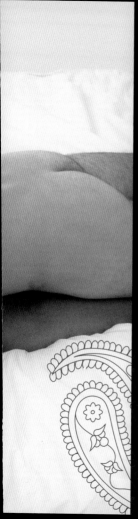

Supine clasping position

02

Side-by-side clasping position

This is similar to the Supine Clasping Position, but instead of the man being on top you both lie on your sides. Vatsyayana specifies that the man should always lie on his left side and the woman on her right. You can roll from a Supine Clasping Position into a Side-by-side Clasping

Position (although it's easier to roll the other way round). This posture enhances your awareness of the subtle sensations of genital contact rather than deep, vigorous thrusts. Neither partner dominates and it's great for soul gazing, hugging, kissing and whispering to one another.

03

He lies on top and penetrates her.
She then bends her knees, puts her feet
flat on the bed and raises her pelvis.
He can thrust inside her or remain still
while she moves her pelvis up and
down. Even if she can't hold this
position for very long it's a sexy
"in-between" position that
allows the man to feel the
eroticism of her body
rising up to meet his.

Widely-opened position

Crab's position

04

She lies on her back, bends her
knees and draws her thighs toward
her stomach. He lies or kneels
between her legs and enters her.
If he holds her knees firmly, she can
relax her legs and feel a powerful
sense of letting go in this position.

Exploring the senses

According to the *Kama Sutra*, foreplay should engage each of our five senses. The "pleasure room" should be fragrant with flowers and perfumes; the couple should drink, play musical instruments and talk, then, as passion builds, they should touch and embrace each other.

Imagine that you are preparing your bedroom for two people who are about to make love for the first time — every detail matters. Think about the colour and texture of your bed linen, the lighting and the music. Try burning incense or essential oils, such as jasmine or ylang ylang. Place chunks of mango and orange segments by the bed for you to suck on before kissing. When you make love try switching the focus of your attention from one sense to another. If you usually concentrate on the sensation of your partner touching you, try thinking about what you see, taste, hear or smell during sex.

05

Pressing position

Begin in a Supine Clasping Position (see page 15), then she bends her legs and presses his body with her thighs. She can do this with her feet flat on the bed or with her thighs raised. To create a compelling sense of intimacy and being quite literally wrapped up in one another, she can rest her calves on his lower back and cross her ankles.

06

Twining position

He lies on top of her and after penetration she raises one leg and wraps it around the back of his thigh (you can also make love in this position when you are standing up; see page 60). Raising her leg in this way gives the woman more control over lovemaking: she can use pressure from her leg to push him in and out. If she is strong and supple enough, she can use the heel of her foot to massage his buttocks or to apply pressure to his perineum (the area between the anus and the genitals) — touching this area can lead to swift and powerful orgasms in some men. To increase or decrease the depth of penetration she can move her leg higher up or lower down his body.

07

Thigh clasp

08

Transverse position

The man lies on his side, facing the woman. He raises his upper leg
and puts it over her hip. Depending on the individual anatomy of
you and your partner, you may find that you can achieve only
shallow penetration in this position. One idea for increasing

the eroticism of the Transverse Position is to use some massage oil on your belly and genitals so that you slip and slide against each other during lovemaking (but don't use oil if you're also using a condom — oil damages latex).

Food for the senses

Sharing food with your lover can be a sexy, intimate or even sacramental act. The aim is to reawaken your senses so make sure that you select foods that have interesting textures, smells and tastes, such as asparagus, oysters, kiwi fruits, honey, caviar, cream and grapes. Dispense with cutlery and use your fingers. Sit down naked on the floor, take your first piece of food and explore it together. For example, gently brush the skin of a kiwi fruit against your lover's lips, then split it open and inhale the fragrance of the flesh before letting the juice drip on to your tongues, down your chins and over your fingers. Some foods, such as frozen grapes or strawberries, are great for swapping between your mouths. When you have touched, smelled, tasted and observed each item of food in your collection, explore all the parts of each other's body in the same way.

hale

xplore

09

Kama's wheel

He sits on the floor or a bed with his legs stretched out in front of him and she then sits astride him with her legs straight out behind his body. You both hold onto each other's upper body. This is a sexy alternative to making love lying down and you can get into it directly from a woman-on-top position. Once you've been in this position for a while, the woman can lie back on the floor or the bed to expose her clitoris and, remaining inside her, the man can bring her to orgasm using his fingers or thumb.

10
Foot clasp

Get into this position in the same way that you got into Kama's
Wheel or use it as a follow-on position from Kama's Wheel.
The difference is that here, instead of holding onto each other's
upper body, you clasp your lover's feet, ankles or shins —

wherever feels most comfortable. This makes it easier to push and pull against each other. She can also lift herself up slightly and, supporting her weight on her hands and feet, move her pelvis so that she massages the head of his penis in her vagina.

11

Bow position

She lies on her back with a pile of
cushions or pillows underneath her.
She has her knees bent and her feet
flat on the bed or floor. He then
enters her from on top. Using props
such as cushions during sex can turn
a familiar position into something
sensational. Experiment with the
number and position of cushions
or pillows until you get it just right.

12

Contrary position

He lies on his back and she lies on top of him with her breasts against his chest and her hands on his waist or thighs. The *Ananga Ranga* instructs the woman to move her hips sharply in a variety of directions. The man can either lie still or guide the

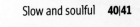

movement of her hips with his hands. For added support, she can rest her hands either side of his body and put her feet on the tops of his, so that she can push against them. The higher up she lies on his body the more clitoral friction she receives.

The sensual tour

If you've been with a lover for a long time it's easy to get into sexual habits that can prevent sex from being a whole-body experience. The sensual tour is a technique designed to slow sex down so that you can fully experience the sensations that you give and receive. It's a great way to rediscover the art of eroticism and, if your sex life is in a rut, this is the way to reinvigorate it. Make sure that you have lots of time and absolute privacy. Don't set out with the aim of reaching orgasm or having sex, just concentrate on touching each other in novel ways and places. Focus on being playful and experimental. Take turns to "tour" each other's body with your hands (or anything else!). As the giver of touch, your aim is to produce new and sensual sensations in your partner's body. As the recipient of touch, your aim is to immerse yourself in sensation.

13
First posture

She lies on her back and raises her legs with her knees bent, he then penetrates her from on top. He can move freely inside her, she can focus on building the intensity of genital sensations as he thrusts, and both of you can enjoy looking at each other. To introduce new sensations, she can move her knees wider apart or raise or lower her legs.

14

She lies on her side and he positions himself between her thighs and enters her. Side-by-side sex positions like this are great for lazy lovemaking when neither of you feels like being on top. If you're having sex on the floor, the Fifth Posture can be the start of a dynamic sequence of positions: start in this posture and then roll into a man-on-top position, such as the First Posture (see page 44), and then over again into a woman-on-top position. From here the woman can sit up and the man can stimulate her clitoris with his hand. The Fifth Posture is also a loving, peaceful position to lie and talk in after you have finished making love.

Fifth posture

15

Eighth posture

She lies on her back and he kneels astride her. The man can't penetrate the woman freely in this posture because her legs are inside rather than outside his. What he can do is hold his penis in his hand and guide it in and out of her vaginal entrance, rubbing his glans in rhythmic circles around her clitoris. This is deeply arousing for both of you.

Self-massage

pinch

rub

squee

Experiment with different forms of touch all over your body to find out what feels good to you. Try stroking your skin with the oiled flats of your palms, applying deep pressure with your thumbs or knuckles, grazing your skin with your fingernails, gently pinching, rubbing and squeezing your flesh between your thumb and fingers; or using a specially designed massage device or even a vibrator. Learn to give yourself a head massage.

...e your fingertips in small, firm circles all over your head or gather fistfuls of your hair and make gentle tugging movements. Try applying pressure with the heels of your hands to the sensitive area above and in front of your ears. More important than mastering specific techniques is to give yourself permission to experience pleasure solely by and for yourself. Be calm, relax and take your time – give yourself up to sensation.

16
The jointer

You both sit facing each other on a bed or the floor and the woman puts her right thigh over the man's left thigh. He then puts his right thigh over her left thigh and you grasp hold of each other. Nefzawi instructs couples to move in a see-saw action, leaning backward and forward in time with the motion of the penis in the vagina.

17

She lies on her left side and he lies on his right side. She puts her top leg over his hip and he stretches his top leg between her legs. This is a gentle and intimate position that is great for slow lovemaking interspersed with plenty of tender kissing. You can get into this position after she has given him oral sex — she simply slides up his body. To up the erotic tempo during side-by-side sex, try scratching each other's buttocks with your fingernails, or sucking each other's fingers in the same rhythm that his penis enters her vagina.

The fusion of love

be more comfortable as her feet rest on the backs of his legs. If the man presses his pelvis tightly against the woman during sex, her clitoris receives lots of friction as he thrusts.

Supported congress • Suspended congress • Congress of a cow
• Knee and elbow standing form • Leg raise • Ninth posture
• Belly to belly • Driving in the peg

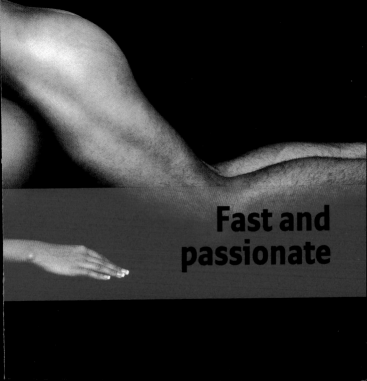

Fast and passionate

19
Supported congress

This is a classic quickie position — you don't even have to get completely undressed. She stands with her back against a wall while he presses his body to hers. She wraps one leg around him — the higher her leg the better — and he enters her. If you enjoy having sex in the shower, try this position.

20

Suspended congress

This position, in which he stands against a wall, lifts her and clasps his hands underneath her buttocks, is perfect for fast sex when you're both at the peak of arousal. She moves up and down on his penis by pushing against the wall with her feet. If you can't do this for long, he can kneel and you can move into the Pressing Position (see page 24).

21

Congress of a cow

She bends over so that her hands touch the floor and the man enters her from behind. This animalistic position evokes powerful feelings of dominance and vulnerability in men and women. The anonymity of this position — in that you can't see each other's faces — can be a huge turn-on. Feel free to indulge your wildest sexual fantasies.

22

Knee and elbow standing form

The man lifts the woman up so that her knees rest in the crooks of his elbows. She wraps her arms around his neck. Although this position demands a fair amount of endurance from the man, the feeling of being so completely held can be a big turn-on for the woman, and the man can enjoy the assertive display of masculine strength.

If you and your partner have strong pubococcygeal (PC) muscles you will feel increased sensations during sex — the vagina grips the penis tightly, you can delay ejaculation and the ripples of orgasm are more intense for both of you. You can strengthen your PC muscles by contracting them for as long as possible and then slowly releasing. (Repeat up to 10 times.) If you find it difficult to locate them, attempt to stop urinating in mid-flow

— the muscles that you contract are your PC muscles. If you're a woman, try massaging your lover's penis by alternately relaxing and contracting them during sex. If you've got really fine muscular control, you may be able to "flutter" your muscles against his penis. If you're a man, you can use your PC muscles to make sex last longer; as you build up to ejaculation, contract your PC muscles as strongly as you can and breathe deeply.

23

Leg raise

There's something effortless about this position in which she presses her body to his and raises one of her legs alongside his body for him to enter her. If he's tall and she's petite, you may be able to achieve only fairly shallow penetration, but you can go deeper if he bends his knees into a semi-squat or if she stands on a slightly raised surface.

24

Ninth posture

25
Belly to belly

You stand face-to-face with your hands around each other's waist. She has her feet wide apart and he has his feet between hers. If couples are a similar height, this can be one of the most erotic positions because you can get into it so quickly. If she is much shorter than him, she can try standing on a raised surface.

26
Driving in the peg

He lifts her up and she puts her arms around his neck and her legs around his waist. She puts her feet on a wall behind her to support some of her weight. He puts his hands around her waist and guides her body. If this position gets tiring, the man can turn around so that the woman's back rests against the wall — great for a passionate mid-sex kiss.

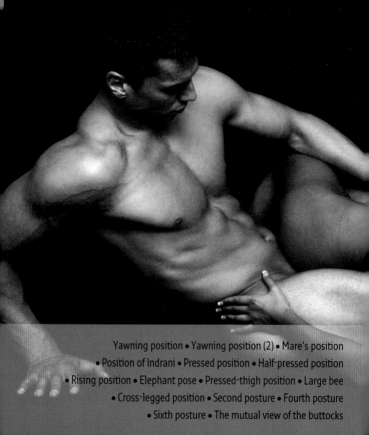

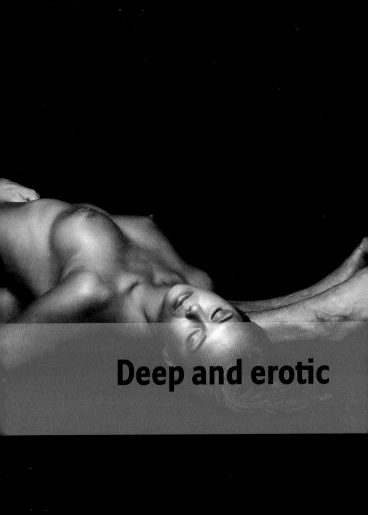

Deep and erotic

27

Yawning position

She lies on her back and raises her legs to rest along the front of his body. He can hold her hands for support as he thrusts. In a variation of this position he can hold onto her feet and gently push them apart (see picture opposite), this will give the sensation that she is opening up to him — she needs to be fairly supple in the groin for this position.

28

Progressing from the Yawning position, she brings her knees to her shoulders and rests her feet on his shoulders. He should start by thrusting slowly and gently. She can give him feedback on what feels good and ask him to speed up or slow down.

Yawning position (2)

29

Mare's position

This is a technique rather than a position. After penetration the woman contracts her love muscles (see pages 68—9) so that the man feels tightly held. You can try this in any position, but it works especially well when the woman sits on the man's lap facing away from him. Once you've perfected the vaginal squeeze, try a pumping action.

Position of Indrani

30

This position, in which the woman draws her knees up to the sides of her body, is recommended in the *Kama Sutra* for the hare man (with a short penis), because it enables the woman to feel deeply penetrated. The elephant man (with a large penis) should take care in this position because penetration can be uncomfortable or even painful if the penis hits the cervix — it's best to go slowly and wait until the woman is extremely aroused (the upper vagina expands and the uterus lifts at the peak of sexual excitement and this creates more space for the penis). You may not be able to have fast and furious sex in this position, but lots of couples rate it as one of the best in terms of intensity and eroticism. Try communicating with your eyes alone.

Touch types

Use your hands, hair, feet, elbows, fingernails, teeth and tongue to stroke, caress and massage your lover's body. Experiment with different pressures. To create the most subtle sensations imaginable, use your exhaled breath as a massage tool; lick a line along the nape of your lover's neck — or any other sensitive part of the body — and then blow gently along the length of that line. Make a "toy box" of props, such as a silk scarf, a tennis ball and a string of beads, and use these to carry out touch experiments on your lover. Stroke each other's inner thighs with your fingernails, slide an ice-cube over her nipples, use a soft paintbrush to stroke his penis and balls, flick the tip of your tongue across the insides of her wrists, or graze the tips of his fingers with your teeth. Massage parts of the body that you might not think of massaging: the ear lobes, the palms of the hands or along the jawline.

31

Pressed position

She lies on her back and draws her knees to her chest. He lifts her and penetrates her in a kneeling position. She can use her fingernails to lightly scratch his thighs or she can stroke her clitoris. She can also add spice by reaching through her thighs and clasping the man's waist with her hands. This allows her to push and pull against him.

32

Half-pressed position

After the Pressed Position (see page 91) she stretches out one of her legs so that her foot points to the ceiling. This changes the sensations she experiences by creating more space in the vagina, and provides a break from the intensity of extremely deep penetration. It's also easier for the woman to stroke her clitoris in this position.

33

She lies on her back with her legs
raised in the air to make a wide "V"
shape (she should spread her legs as
far apart as she can) and he leans
between her legs to enter her. An
advantage of the Rising Position for
the man is that he can lean back and
watch his penis moving in and out of
her vagina. If the depth of the penis
feels too intense in this position, she
can bend her knees and put her feet
on the bed. If she wants to be
penetrated more deeply, she can draw
her knees to her chest. Experiment
with the angle of her legs to find out
what feels best for both of you.

Rising position

34
Elephant pose

She lies on her front and he enters her from behind. To increase the depth of penetration, the woman can spread her legs very widely. You can also place one or more pillows or cushions under the woman's pelvis

to make her vaginal entrance more accessible. Women can also enhance their enjoyment by concentrating on the sensations emanating from the G-spot as the man massages the front wall of her vagina with his penis.

Pleasuring her *yoni*

Coat your hands with massage oil and press one palm flat on your lover's vulva to allow her to enjoy the sensation spreading slowly through her genitals and pelvis. Now use your hand to stroke the length of her from front to back. Massage and gently tweak her inner and outer labia. Now gently slide your longest finger into her vagina (as she becomes more aroused, you can insert more fingers). Explore the inside of her vagina by

slide

lick

moving your finger(s) up and down and round and round. Now withdraw your finger(s) and, without breaking contact, use your index finger to draw slow, gentle circles around the area of her clitoris. After a while alternate this with light flicking or tickling of her clitoris. Now put your finger(s) back in her vagina, but this time rest the pad of your thumb against her clitoris so that, as you move your fingers in and out, her clitoris is stimulated too.

late

35

Pressed-thigh position

She lies on her back, raises her legs in the air and presses her thighs closely together. She can rest her legs over one of his shoulders or along the centre of his body. He can hold onto her thighs as he thrusts in and out of her or he can slide his hands underneath her buttocks and lift her up and down. Some women find it easier to contract their love muscles (see pages 68—9) tightly around the penis when their thighs are pressed together in this position — try it.

37

Cross-legged position

Begin in a woman-on-top position: he lies on his back and she sits astride him. When you're ready to change position, he crosses his legs while lying down and pushes himself up into a sitting position. He keeps his legs crossed and she sits on his lap with her legs resting either side of him. He can place his hands on her shoulders. You can't move freely in this position, but it's wonderful for letting your bodies melt into each other and kissing passionately. If you enjoy using sex toys, it's easy to incorporate a vibrator into this position; she can hold the tip against her clitoris. Alternatively, she can lie back on the bed and he can stimulate her with a vibrator or his hand.

Pleasuring his *lingam*

Coat your hands in oil and rest one hand on his penis and testicles. Then enclose his penis in the palms of both hands. Roll his shaft gently between your palms, then interlock your fingers and bring the heels of your hands together so that his penis is completely encircled. If his penis is long enough (or erect), rest the pads of your thumbs on his frenulum (the strip of skin that attaches the foreskin to the shaft). Now tighten your grip and glide

roll

tip

your interlocked hands along the length of his shaft and over the top of his glans. Use varying pressures and speeds — you can introduce a twisting motion if you like. You can also use the tip of your index finger to trace a line from the tip of his glans all the way down to his perineum and anus, or hold the base of his penis firmly in one hand while you use the pad of the thumb on your other hand to massage his frenulum in tiny circles.

38

Second posture

This position demands a lot of
suppleness from the woman: she
lies on her back and raises her legs
so that her toes are over her ears.
He gets on top and enters her.
Well-endowed men should move
very gently in the Second Posture
because the vagina is contracted
and vigorous thrusting can
be uncomfortable.

39

Fourth posture

She lies on her back and puts her
legs over his shoulders. Her lower
body rests along the front of his
thighs so that her pelvis is raised.
The man's penis is exactly opposite
the woman's vulva in this position.
She can use her hands to stroke
his thighs, or her breasts or clitoris.
As he moves inside her, he can ask
for guidance about speed and depth.

40

Sixth posture

She rests on her knees and elbows and he enters her in a kneeling position. He can use his hands to hold her buttocks, to stroke her breasts and nipples or to move her body back and forth. She can deepen penetration by lowering her upper body to the floor or make it more shallow by kneeling upright so that her body is parallel to his.

The mutual view of the buttocks

41

He lies on his back and she sits on top facing away from him and guides his penis into her body. He bends his knees and uses his thighs to squeeze her. She leans forward and touches the floor with her hands. You can see the curves of each other's buttocks in this position and, if she moves up and down on him, you can both watch the penis as it glides in and out of the vagina. In a variation on this position she can sit upright and hold onto his knees. He can caress her buttocks and draw his fingertips down her back for a spine-tingling effect when she is close to orgasm.

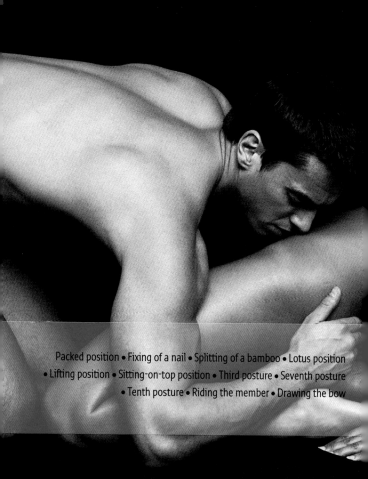

Packed position • Fixing of a nail • Splitting of a bamboo • Lotus position
• Lifting position • Sitting-on-top position • Third posture • Seventh posture
• Tenth posture • Riding the member • Drawing the bow

Adventurous
and thrilling

42

Packed position

She lies on her back, raises her legs
in the air and crosses them. She can
either rest her crossed legs on his
shoulder after he has entered her
or he can treat her legs as a vertical
pole to hold on to. The woman
has little freedom to move in this
position and the element of female
surrender and male dominance
can be arousing for both of you.

43

Fixing of a nail

In this playful position she stretches one leg out on the floor or bed and rests the heel of her other foot on his forehead. Her raised foot acts as a hammer that knocks the nail — his head! — into a wall. For her to keep her heel on his forehead, lovemaking needs to be slow and considered rather than fast and furious.

44

Splitting of a bamboo

In this dynamic pose the woman changes the positions of her legs throughout lovemaking. She starts with one leg hooked over the man's shoulder and one leg stretched out on the floor or bed. Then she moves the upright leg down and the stretched leg up (he can help her lift her legs up and down). She keeps alternating

her legs like this for as long as you both hold the position. The main benefit of this is that the angle of the penis in the vagina keeps changing, producing a variety of sensations for both of you. Depending on the suppleness of the woman, the man can lie on top and kiss her mouth or kneel in an upright position.

45

The Lotus is an advanced yoga pose
that you should practise by yourself
before you attempt it during sex.
Sit on the floor or bed in an upright
position. Bend your right leg and tuck
your right heel tightly into your left
hip socket. Now lift your left foot up
onto your right thigh as close to your
right hip socket as you can. Even
sustaining this yoga pose for a short
time on a regular basis will improve
the flexibility of your hips and groin.
Now try this pose while lying down
and let your lover enter you. Some
women enjoy the tight, compact
nature of this position during sex, but
it may be hard to maintain. If you find
the position difficult or uncomfortable,
just cross your legs instead.

Lotus position

Mouth strokes for her

Experiment with these strokes. Ask her for plenty of feedback about what she enjoys or ask her to lick or suck the tip of your little finger in the way that she would like you to stimulate her clitoris.

- Flick the tip of your tongue side to side or back and forth on her clitoris.
- Press your lips around her clitoral hood and suck, using your tongue to flick, lick or stroke her clitoris.
- Make your tongue relaxed and flat, and make broad tongue strokes

across the entire clitoral area.

- Use the point of your tongue to circle her clitoris — vary the speed.
- Put your first two fingers flat on either side of her clitoral hood and then squeeze them together to push her clitoris up and out. Now very gently lick her clitoris.
- Use your tongue on her clitoris while you insert your longest fingers into her vagina and massage her G-spot all the way to orgasm.

46

He sits with his legs out in front of him and she sits on his lap with her legs hooked over his elbows. Her feet are off the floor or bed and he holds her body with his hands. The *Ananga Ranga* suggests that the man lifts the woman and moves her from left to right on his penis (but not up or down) until the "supreme moment". The woman can support some of her body weight by leaning back on her hands.

Lifting position

47

He lies on his back and she sits cross-legged on top of him. Either partner can control the rhythm and pace of lovemaking: he can grasp her waist and move her backward and forward or she can wriggle and rock

her pelvis and squeeze her love muscles around him (see pages 68—9). The man has the added eroticism of being able to watch her masturbate to orgasm in this position.

48

Third posture

He lies on top of her with one of her legs under his arm and her other leg over his shoulder. Although she doesn't have much freedom of movement, she can wriggle her hips and contract her love muscles around his penis (see pages 68—9). It's also easy for her to touch her nipples and clitoris with her fingers in this position.

49

Seventh posture

Mouth strokes for him

These eight oral sex techniques should be performed one after the other:

- Nominal Congress: hold his penis in your hand and caress the top with your lips and tongue.
- Biting the Sides: hold the tip of his penis with your fingers and nuzzle and nibble the sides of his shaft.
- Outside Pressing: press your lips around his glans in a tight seal and move your mouth up and down, sucking as you do so.

nuzzle

- **Inside Pressing:** take as much of his penis into your mouth as you can and press your lips around his shaft.
- **Kissing:** hold his penis in your hand and cover it with kisses.
- **Rubbing:** lick his penis and swirl your tongue around his glans.
- **Sucking a Mango Fruit:** enclose the top half of his penis in your mouth and suck.
- **Swallowing it Up:** take his whole penis into your mouth and suck.

& nibble

50
Tenth posture

She lies back on the bed, grasping the headboard firmly, and clasps his hips with her legs. He enters her, lifting up her pelvis as he does so. She uses her leg muscles to push and pull herself back and forth on his penis. He synchronizes his rhythm with hers. If it's difficult to move in this position, the woman can drop her hips back down onto the bed.

51

Riding the member

He lies down with a cushion under his shoulders and raises his knees toward his shoulders. She stands astride him and lowers herself onto his penis. Either she moves up and down on him by bending her knees, or he moves her with his legs while she grasps his knees or shoulders for support. Try leaning in so that your faces are nearly touching.

52

Drawing the bow

She lies on her side and he lies behind her between her legs. He puts one or both of his hands on her shoulders and she grasps his feet and pulls them toward her. Joined in this way you form the shape of a bow and arrow. The excitement of this position comes from its novelty. She can heighten sensation by squeezing and massaging his toes or he can run his fingers down the length of her back. If you feel a sense of freedom and anonymity in this position, make the most of it by indulging in a favourite fantasy.